do your face fit?

Poems about fitting in and standing out

Compiled by
Roger Stevens

For Joseph and his students

Nasen would like to thank Roger Stevens,
David Parkins and all the contributing poets for
their time and commitment to this project.

nasen
Helping Everyone Achieve

Contents

The Meaning of Life

Love and Friendship

Hope

I sit by the window
As the sky grows dark
Watching the road
From your house to the park

As you walk past the window
You see me and grin
I glance up – our eyes meet –
I wave – Come on in!

I open the front door
My face has gone red
I bring us two Cokes
(There is much left unsaid)

There's a film at the Showcase
We both want to see
I suggest that we go there
You quickly agree

I sit by the window
The street lights come on
If you had passed – I wonder
What would I have done?

Roger Stevens

Lisa

Do you fancy Lisa?
Who? Do you mean Lisa who's got
curly, dyed auburn hair with subtle
silvery streaks, deep green eyes that
you could dive into like a dolphin, a cute
sort of dimply chin, luscious lips under a
slightly turned-up nose, ears with gold
studs, runs like a gazelle, plays wing
attack at netball, clever with computers,
got a cat called 'Superpuss', supports
the same soccer team as me, lives at
41 Lennox Lane, by the bus shelter,
phone number 534337 and has two
much younger sisters?
Yes, that Lisa.
Can't say I've really noticed her.

Mike Johnson

Mutual Wish

If only I was Natalie,
I'd have everything going for me.
She's a brilliant friend – we gossip no end.
I just wish she was me.
She's cool and quick, knows every trick,
makes things happen, makes life tick.
I'm her reverse – I make things worse.
It really makes me sick!
But guess what she said, right out of the blue,
yesterday in the dinner queue!
I was grabbing a tray, when I heard her say:
"You know, I wish I was you!"

Kate Williams

Left Out Together

There's the crowd of them again,
The boys with their girls,
Carefree,
Laughing and chatting and going somewhere –
Not including me.
They never say
"Why don't you come too?"
I wander away
And pretend I don't care –
But I do.
And when they come back
They've got it all to remember
And share.
I wouldn't know.
I wasn't there.

 I tried once to be friends with a girl;
Well, actually, I've tried twice.
But – this is the truth –
I've always thought
That you looked quiet and nice.
You look as though
You might be feeling the same:
Left on the sidelines,
Out of the game... ?
You are?
I was actually wondering whether
We could team up and both be
Left out together.

Eric Finn

What Happened

He came in through the double doors
out of the rain,
looked up and saw me
then...
Was it my brain?
Was it a heart attack
or indigestion
or something catching?
That's the big question.
All I know is that he blushed
just a little bit,
then he almost smiled at me
but I noticed it.
After that, things went mad:
my face went bright red,
my heart started thumping wildly,
so did my head.
By then he'd disappeared –
gone the other way.
Still, I had this strange feeling
all through the day.
Next time I saw him coming
I thought I'd die
but he never looked at me
and just walked by.

Jill Townsend

Feelings

Feelings?

I don't talk about them.

I write down how I'm feeling
in my Feelings Diary.

That helps.

And when I'm fine
I don't write a line.

My diary's almost full.

Bernard Young

The Lost Valentine

He put it in the post box,
The slight thud as it hit the bottom
Recoiled like a gun fired inside his head;
He fought the sudden urge to claim it back
And walked away, his heart pounding.

She opened the empty letterbox
And her heart sank;
As another Valentine's Day passed
She cried herself to sleep.

Somewhere,
The lost valentine rests forgotten;
Wishing maybe someday
He will be remembered.

Violet Macdonald

What Jason Has

I wish that I had Jason's hair
with thick and wavy curls.
I wish I had his confidence
when talking to the girls.
I wish I had his lazy walk.
I wish I had his style.
I wish I had his muscles,
and I wish I had his smile.
I wish I had his shark tattoo
(though that may be a rumour).
I wish I had his stories
and his wicked sense of humour.
I guess I wish an awful lot,
but one thing you can bet;
Of all the things that Jason has,
I wish I had Annette.

Eric Ode

I Don't Get It

They say we have much in common
We both have a pretty quick wit
And she can tell a humorous tale
But I don't get it

Her mind is as sharp as her pencil
And they say that we make a good fit
They say that there's magic in her designs
But I don't get it

Her kisses are coloured Kandinsky
Her body is Rubens (well, a bit)
But the key to her heart is Picasso
And I don't get it

Roger Stevens

Chat Up Lines

I'm drained from drinking
Fatigued with flirting
Deadbeat from dancing
Exhausted with talking
I need resuscitating...
How's your mouth-to-mouth?

Philip Waddell

Being Laddish

It was just a quick snog
behind the bog
and a little peck
on the neck
for goodness' sake.
Big mistake.

Now she feels
I'm head over heels
and want to date her
when really my mates were
behind it. I swear
it was only a dare.

Jill Townsend

I Asked My Mum to Get Me This Top

I explained how I wanted one
Just like the girl in that advert.
She pulled this out of the bag.
'It's almost the same,' she said
'But I couldn't get that colour
and the neck's scoopier
and the design on the front's different
and it's longer.
Is it longer?
Yeah, I think it's longer...
Definitely. Longer.
Oh, and it's cotton, not Lycra.
But apart from that
It's identical.
Like it? What d'ya think?'

Jan Dean

Wardrobe Crisis

Purple spot or
Yellow stripe?
What shall I wear to go out tonight?
Slinky black or
Day-glo bright?
Which will dazzle in the disco light?
Slick, short skirt or
Long and swirly?
Do I want to be glam or girlie?
Sleek, straight bob or
Crimped and curly?
Lucky I started two hours early!

Julia Rawlinson

Kiss Me Again

Kiss me again
like the last time,
but better.
Kiss me again
for longer.
Kiss me again
till I'm dizzy
with holding my breath,
till my skin sings
till I grow wings
till I dance in the sky...
If you don't kiss me again
I'll die.

Jan Dean

Disco-O-O

The music beats a rhythm in my head (head
head),
And I wish that I was snuggled up in bed (bed
bed),
Because when the strobe light flashes what I see
(see see),
Is my boy kissing a girl who isn't me (me me).
So I find a corner where it's dark and dim (dim
dim),
And I watch the way she wraps herself round him
(him him),
And I know that this will be the night we part
(part part),
And the dancers stomp the pieces of my heart
(heart heart).
So I tell myself I'm big and brave and strong
(strong strong),
And I kid myself that I can carry on (on on),
But then all at once I know it's really true (true
true),
Because suddenly I'm dancing here with you (you
you).

Julia Rawlinson

After the Party

I wake up
in the middle of the night
on the stairs

Someone
has put a blanket on me
And drawn on my face
with eyeliner.

Celinu Macdonald

Rainbow Girl:
A Holiday Romance

Red were her lips
(she was always licking
strawberry ice-lollies).
Orange was her mobile
(she had a million friends,
back in Aberdeen).
Yellow was her T-shirt
(I bought a matching one,
at the cheapo beach shop).
Green were my friends
(she went to the indoor salt-
water pool with me).
Blue was what I felt
(after our final big bust-up,
at the end of the pier).
Indigo is my huge bruise
(she could kick pretty hard,
even in flip-flops)!
Violet is my new girlfriend
(she's from Bristol and
is here another week).

Mike Johnson

What My Mother Said

My mother always used to say,
When I sat sobbing at tea,
"Don't worry my girl, you're gorgeous
And there's plenty more fish in the sea!

"Now wave him goodbye, he's far too shallow
Just trust me, you'll have what you wish!"
"Well, thank you so much for your helpful advice
But I couldn't get off with a fish."

Andrew Fusek Peters and Polly Peters

No Thanks

She is asking me to a sleep over
but I'd rather sleep over a volcano
or a termite heap
than spend the night with her
she's a total creep.
Her mates are just as bad,
the ones that aren't stupid
are just plain mad.
Me, join that lot?
I don't think so, wouldn't sink low.
Hang with them?
Even a rabid bat would not do that.
Asking me to a sleep over – she's mental.
Smiling like a nutter – she's dental.
If she was on fire I wouldn't spit
that's the long and short of it.
I can't stand her lame crowd.
Why's she looking daggers at me?

Oh, did I say all that out loud?

Jan Dean

Initials

"Louis 4 Emma"
lay between the inked-in,
stabbed-out hollows, beside a
"Screw U Armstrong" and graphic tits.
Behind the smoke-screen of a book
I carved, in emulation, "T.P. L J.D."
The action almost made me flush and
set a kind of seal on what I dreamt might come.
Strange as I hardly knew the girl.
But I was grateful in those unheeding lessons
as five rough letters
drew me to her like a song.
Soon a change of classroom held
"Duggan is a slag".
Abrupt, emptying disillusion –
that wounding absence of her first name.

Trevor Parsons

Why?

Why is there love?
Why is there hate?
Why am I good?
Why not just great?
Why are there slow songs?
Why aren't you here?
Why far away?
Why not so near?
Why is there hope?
Why is there fear?
Why should I listen
When you whisper in my ear?
When should I leave?
Why should I stay?
Why am I still here
While you drift away?
When can I text you?
And be sure you'll reply?
You say you truly like me
Then why do you deny?
I can't trust you anymore
Why do you ask?
Why are you oblivious
While you make me masked?

Paige

Perfect Blend

She's a:
Sadness safe cracker,
A down-in-the-dumps hijacker.
A deepest secret keeper,
A talk-for-hours non-sleeper
An automatic advice dispenser,
A future candidate for Mensa.
An Olympic-qualifying talker,
A hold-head-high-whatever walker.
A listener to all my woes,
A fear-of-God to all my foes
A promise-fulfiller, gossip killer,
Dance-all-nighter, tiredness fighter,
Solid shoulder for things I've told her.
She's my:
Round the bend, got to spend
Quick to lend, own trend
Perfect blend
Best friend!
(What would I do without her?)

Andrew Fusek Peters and Polly Peters

What is

In the dark
between
what is going to be
and what is,
I found him.
He had
no fear.
I told him mine.
He was far
from hope.
I gave him mine.
He had
no friends.
I brought him mine,
and he
unfurled
his heart of light,
and we spun
a silver
moonlit space
in the dark,
between
what is going to be
and what is.

Liz Brownlee

Work and Play

Outside

The others play.
They flick their pony tails,
And jump rope in their shiny shoes.
They glance at me in passing,
And then turn their haughty heads away
In unison, down heads into a huddle,
And laugh their secret, special laugh,
High pitched and musical.
I stand on one leg, awkwardly,
Wobble and watch the ground,
Pretending to be interested in ants.
I hang around,
Hoping that one day they will let me in,
And let that happy childhood
That the grown-up people talk about so wistfully
Begin.

Julia Rawlinson

Let Me Be Involved

I may be blind
But let me be involved
I may not be fast
It doesn't matter if I come last
I might be deaf
You think it doesn't matter because I can't hear you

I might be quiet
But I still want to be heard
I may be in a wheelchair
But I still want to do the things I love to do

Luke Petty

Playground Wanderer

Am I invisible?

Because
you don't seem to see
me.

Because
you don't seem to see
how I have to wander around
that playground.

Because
you don't seem to see
that every breaktime
is a lifetime
of waiting
for the bell
to ring.

But
you do know me
and by many names.

New kid.
Bright kid.
Odd kid.
Big kid.
Misfit.
Or just plain
different.

Can you see me now?

James Carter

Respect

My name is Lewis and my school is Friary
I say inclusion is top priority
Now some people say that inclusion's bad
To those people I say, Then I think you're sad.
You don't know what it's like to be me!
And that's why I go to Friary.
So when I hit the corridor I don't go for no stroll,
Me I get in my wheels and roll man roll
And if they stand in my way I mow them down!
So you'd best show respect when Lewis is around.

Lewis Armour

Foundation Stone

When we play football in games
I'm the last on the pitch
It takes me longer to get dressed, you see
And longer to do up my boots
It's the dyspraxia
Makes me clumsy
I'm all fungers and thimbs

But I can kick the ball
Mr Stanton says I have
A monster kick of mega-power
Unfortunately
I do not have pin-point accuracy

I've lost three balls already this year.
One on the roof
One in the back of a lorry
Heading for the M1
And one in the cement mixer
Where it will become
Part of the new community centre.

In years to come
I'll tell my kids
See that building?
I helped with the foundations.

Roger Stevens

Name Calling

They called me frog-face with ears like a bat.
I said, 'I'm not – I'm worse than that.'

They called me rat-nose with a tongue like a shoe.
I said, 'Is that the best you can do?'

They called me mouse-eyes, skunk breath, dog-head.
I said, 'I'm worse than all that you've said.'

They said, 'It's no fun calling you a name.'
I called, 'That's a pity – I'm enjoying this game.'

Charles Thomson

Inclusion

I am what I am
My name is Jenny Davenport
I am fourteen years old
I struggle with maths
I don't know the answers
I struggle with working with others
I can't say what I want to say
I can't answer the question
Because I don't know much about it
But I can...
Be a good friend
Even though I drive people round the bend!
Make people laugh and have fun!
Even though I am on the run!
Work hard in PD and RE
I wear glasses so I can see!
I AM what I AM...
And I know that I CAN
Be as sweet as strawberry jam.

Jenny Davenport

What My Careers Advisor Said

You could build a career in construction,
Explore the possibilities of travel
Or aim for the army.
Maybe your fortune lies in astrology?
You might shape a profession in sculpting
And I'm sure you could cut it as a hairdresser
But I can't picture you as a photographer
And you couldn't hold a position in modelling.
Then again you could compete for a place as a runner
Or go for some post as a messenger
Or steer towards driving a taxi.
Failing all that you might consider philosophy!
But I really don't see you as an optician
And can't believe you'd make it as a priest
And your form doesn't suggest teaching.
As for writing – cross that off straight away!

Philip Waddell

Wall

He sits in the damp shade
with his thoughts; his back to the wall.
And a football's heavy thud
against brick, and the laughter.

He makes lists of the creatures
that hide behind climbers, in crevices:
woodlice, spiders, aphids and snails.
Calculates their number in hundreds.

He sits with his back to the wall;
imagines himself painting it.
Names in his head, the colours he'd mix:
moss green, burnt sienna, ochre.

Rachel Rooney

There Was No Other Way

There was no other way and I was small enough.
They were drunk and arguing.
His wrapped fist broke the window.
He knocked out most of the glass.
I took off my winter coat.
He lifted me up and began to post me through.
She said she was freezing and to hurry up.
I was frightened about the drop on the other side.
He said I'd be O.K.
She said to hurry up she was bloody freezing.
He didn't say anything when she pushed.
I felt the blood run down into my eyes.
At the end of term she got the school photographer
to paint out the scar
before the photo was sent to Gran.
I wanted a key of my own.

Cathy Benson

Difficult Times

Life is difficult
Well, in my early years
I used to use my mouth and feet
Instead of my brain and ears

I have emotional problems
I was always in aggression mode
Which was hard to crack
Like the Da Vinci Code

I always had emotional problems
It was so hard to crack
But it was not my fault
Because I have my dad to thank for that

I used to get into fights at school
A place called Joe Bloggs infants
They treated me like a no-good child
But nobody knew the difference

They were a rubbish school
Because they held me back for two years
They just used judgement
Instead of their eyes and ears

Then I went to Portal House
They were great!
They were a specialist school
They were the ones that set me straight

And now I am at St Anthony's
Not doing any fighting
I'm great in every lesson in school and college
And I'm brilliant at my reading and writing

Bret Linsdell

Joke

Jade says
She's not going to school today
Jade says
She has better things to do
Watch the breakfast show
Compose a letter to the classroom flirt
Make a face
Iron her shortest skirt
Read the gossip magazines
Dish some dirt
For the morning's big retail adventure
Ride the forty-three then wander through the
Marchbank Centre
Eat a slimline burger and a diet coke
Visit the graveyard
Watch the shadows race across the grass
Sit beneath the withered oak
And in her head recite the words that trace her
mother's grave
And wonder, is it all a joke?

Roger Stevens

The Dyslexic Poet

There are kids who get no credit
Who you write off in your edit
Who are not "dum" but dyslexic

I don't think about it like you think about it
But I don't see how that makes me thick
I'm dyslexic, though I can't even spell it
Which is really stupid isn't it?

But no, sir, I'm not so thick
You said it sir, but I forget it
My concentration went and quit
I read it miss but I didn't get it

Now there'll be more red crosses than red ticks
But no sir, I'm not no twit
You've got it wrong, you say I'm crazy
You say I'm pathetic but you just don't get it, miss

There's a word, sir, you should check it
There's a word, miss, you must've read it
And if you think I'm thick, you say I'm lazy,
I get by on my sheer wit and I don't regret it

So, miss, give us a big red tick!
But don't you see
I'm a dyslexic poet

Justin Coe

Entering a Castle

Don't enter a castle quietly
or timidly,
don't enter it anxiously,
ready to bolt
 at the slightest sound.
Don't enter it stealthily
taking slow and thoughtful steps,
considering with each footfall
the mystery of history.
Don't be meek
or frightened to speak.
For when you enter a castle
you should charge through the gate
and signal your arrival with a SHOUT!
You should play the invading army
and barge a way through.
You should swagger up to the door
Then shove it aside and announce,
"Here I am. This is mine!"

The castle is here, it is waiting for you,
And today,
It is yours for the taking!

Brian Moses

The Meaning of Life

Broken

I'm gasping for air,
My legs have gone numb.
My fingers are twitching.
Please help me someone.

My stomach's all hollow.
I'm feeling uneasy.
I'm starting to panic,
It's making me queasy.

I don't know what
I am going to do next.
My mobile is broken
and I just have to text.

Doda Smith

Pimple Pimple

Pimple, pimple,
little spot –
how I wish
that you were not
throbbing on my
nose so bright
like a flashing
traffic light.
Pimple, pimple,
now you're here –
how I wish
you'd disappear!

Graham Denton

Fly

A fly hits its head
Against the window

Going in circles
Trying to get out

Sometimes
I know how it feels.

Violet Macdonald

Paranoia

The guy
in the
suit and tie
let out
a sigh
as I
walked by

Why?

Bernard Young

Drop in the Ocean

Sloshing around
in life's restless sea,
there's a drop in the ocean –
and that drop is me.
Riding the waves,
or washed up on the shore,
I'm a minuscule drop
among zillions more.

I'm a drop in the ocean
of life's restless sea –
but there'd be no ocean
without drops like me!

Jane Clarke

A Speck of Dust

A speck of dust that floats on by
A raindrop falling from the sky
A tiny pebble on the beach
Too small to notice
Insignificant
Our little world is only one
Amidst a million raging suns
The vastness of the universe
Too huge to comprehend
Magnificent.

Andrea Shavick

Ted Teenager

Sunday 6am,
Baby wakes, baby screams,
Mum moans, Dad grunts,
Feet pad,
Ted dreams.
Sunday 10am,
Sun shines, birds cheep,
Head out to feed the ducks,
Doors slam,
Ted sleeps.
Sunday 1pm,
Settle down to pie and chips,
Food smells fill the house,
Pans bang,
Ted kips.
Sunday 6pm,
Dad starts on the chores,
Mum gives babe a bath,
Water splashes,
Ted snores.
Sunday 10pm,
Doors locked, lights out,
Mum and Dad fall into bed,
They snore,
Ted shouts...
"MORNING EVERYONE! WHAT'S FOR
BREAKFAST?"

Julia Rawlinson

Mermaid's Lament

I've had enough of perching on rocks
stinking of fish, waiting for sailors
to pass by and fall in love.

I want to swim away to shore,
stand up on my own two feet and walk
tall across dry land.

I want to go disco dancing with mates,
look great in my high-heeled stilettos
and tight blue jeans.

I want to pedal hard up a steep hill,
Then, legs outstretched, freewheel down
just for the fun of it.

I want to be a striker, take a penalty
and score the golden goal, perform cartwheels
to a roaring crowd.

Or simply lounge on the beach in a twin-set bikini,
paint my toenails, and watch the fishermen
emptying out their nets.

Rachel Rooney

Sleepover

I'm going round to Kerry's on my way
because she's got this new top that I want.
And maybe if her mum says it's O.K.
I'll sleep over. But if she says I can't
I'll go down to the bus station to see
if any of my other mates are there
and we'll hang out, just talking, possibly
go for a walk. Whatever. I don't care.
Mum's got her new boyfriend round tonight.
He winks at me as if I were a kid.
He must be joking! I keep out of sight.
She likes it that way. Gives me a few quid.
I grab my stuff up quick and disappear.
"Don't worry, I'd rather be dead than here."

Jill Townsend

Our House

The air in our house
never moves.

It's stuffy with stifled hope.
Threats hang in the air
and fear.
And no one dare shout
in case it all falls down,
it all comes out.
All the hates and the hurts
and the disappointments,
the thousand swallowed questions,
the tears caught in the throat.

We move quietly
or not at all.
We shrink in shadows
quiet, small.
We don't smile or laugh out loud
or cry or scream or shout.
We don't make a show.
We don't let it out.
We stay out of the way

The doors are shut.
The windows tight.
Our voices low.
The only light –
the TV glow.
We turn the sound up.

We hold ourselves in.
We don't make a show.

We don't make a din.
We hold our breath.

That's why the air in our house
never moves.

Michaela Morgan

My Life

She chose to have me taken away, my mum.
I was only young when I got moved on.
I know I was sad,
She took me to the park,
I have photos to prove it.
That's when I said goodbye, at Farming World.

I'm angry now.
She kept my brother, not me.
I was scared then, I didn't understand,
I do now.
She was young, not as young as me. I didn't hear
any more, she's gone missing.
I'm worried she's dead.
I still love her... sort of!

Amy Staff

Sam's Story

My Mammy died when I was six years old.
I cried and cried. I didn't understand.
Where had she gone to? When would she come
home?
They talked about some glorious Wonderland.

I had bad dreams. I saw no magic land.
When I was nine, my Daddy married Dee.
Though she was kind and kissed and cuddled me
I hated her for what she could not be.

When I was twelve I stole a stick of gum
From Gracie's Corner Shop. That felt well good!
I nicked two tubes of glue, a mag, some cigs.
And then they caught me. Well, I knew they
would.

I'm fifteen now. I sit right at the back.
The teachers pick on me. I stare them out.
I smile, they don't like that, lean back and smile.
And once I've left I'll make those losers shout.

Gerard Benson

A Mate's Funeral

He wouldn't normally
have given him
flowers

Celina Macdonald

Fred

Cried a silly old fellow called Fred,
"Alas! I am dead. I am dead!"
But they answered, "What rot.
You are not. You are not,
You lazy thing. Get out of bed."

Gerard Benson

The Struggle

Two bows.
Two bows upon her head,
Two bows holding the bandage up,
Two bows I see above her eyes,
Two bows I wish weren't there,
Two bows because of the hole in her head,
Two bows I remember,
Two bows, the spectacular speech vanished,
Two bows that are special,
Two bows, two aneurisms it all fits,
Two bows I love as much as the woman,
My mom, the woman with the two bows.

Abby Keffeler

No One Understands

I wake up each morning
In a different way
And no one understands
No one understands
Performing tough procedures
Five times a day
No one understands
No one
No over-night camps
Or trips out with mom
No string bikinis
I just can't calm
No one understands
No one
Unkind memories
Embedded in my brain
No one understands
No one understands
Too much pain
No one understands
No one
Are you an "Inny" or an "Outty"?
Why red not blue?
Is it a pill or a liquid?
Why do you have to?
And no one understands...
No one will

Paige

Nothing Personal

We can't have you in here
But please understand
That we've nothing against you.
If it was up to us
But it isn't. It's our customers.
It isn't personal.

If we let you in
Then word would get around.
We have to make a living
And times are hard.
We can't let you sit there
But please understand
That we don't make the rules.
If we did
It wouldn't be like this.
It isn't personal.
There's room at the back
And as things are
You'll feel much safer
If you know your place.
We can't let you join
But please understand
That if we could
We would. It's the other teams
We play against...
It isn't personal.
They think your kind
Are trouble
And that where you come from
It's a different game.

We can't say why
But please understand
It's how things are.
They've always been like this
Although it does seem wrong.
It's nothing personal
But what can we do?
Try to see it our way.
If it was up to us
We'd welcome you.

John Mole

On My Birthday

As food is thrown
And games are played
And drinks are downed
And mess is made
And riots run
And damage done
I'm the only one
Not having fun.

Celina Macdonald

The Trouble is...

Like jigsaw pieces from a different box
Like faulty plugs that have a broken pin
Like some odd key that won't undo the locks
The trouble is... I don't fit in.

Like heavy black bin-bags to empty or
Like muddy balls and boots when adults shout
Like rinsed milk bottles lined up at the door
The trouble is... I am left out.

But unlike jigsaw pieces, plugs or key
And all those other things I mentioned there
I'm not an object. I can think and feel.
The trouble is... I just don't care.

Rachel Rooney

What I Fear

Weekday lunchtime, city centre,
hour of snacks and banter,
a mugging gets under way.
Passers-by pass blindly by,
lookers-on look on –
a mugging is soon done.
When one young and good Samaritan
breaks ranks to help another
and is stabbed for his bother.
Blood blooms, three youths scatter,
the lookers-on and passers-by now gather.
One life, one mobile phone lie almost lost.
And later will those three youths boast
their bravery and breakneck flight
and toast the one who holds and held the knife?
And later, in the empty hours, at last alone,
in his own and ordinary room,
will he relive the vicious punch line of that thrust,
its bone-led blunder through the chest?
See again the startling blood, hear the cry
and tighten up his eyes and shudder lightly?
Will he sicken at his own quick rage,
stare into bravado's grave
and start, instinctively, to care?
Or won't he? That's what I fear.

Trevor Parsons

Just a Small War

We're watching the usual war pictures
On the six o'clock news on the box:
Shells exploding, bodies lying,
Fires, tanks, roadblocks.
Dave says, "Course, that's just a small war.
I'm not sure who's fighting who.
For real wars you have to go back
To World Wars One and Two."

On the screen, in her shattered house,
A woman picks around for her stuff.

Bet she doesn't think it's a small war.
Bet she thinks it's real enough.

Eric Finn

Frank

Perhaps it was a glass of red wine
At Christmas. Just a sip
From the whisky flask at grandpa's hip
And then, another time

His father's vodka, hidden well
Behind the beers. He drank a cup
And secretly he made it up
With water. He knew his mum would never tell.

Soon half the bottle's gone
And he moves on. His mate's dad owns the
Gilded Cockatoo
And doesn't miss a pint or two
It's good clean fun.

I joined them once. A long and scary night.
His uncle's caravan behind the hill
Teacher's whisky. Half a bottle.
I puked up. I was so ill.
My guts poured out my head. I guess it served
me right.

I picture Frank, a toothless grin, a wink
He sitting in the doorway of a vacant shop
Half thinking maybe he should stop
Drinking. He sees me staring and asks me for a
pound to buy a drink.

Roger Stevens

My Week in Politics

Monday I thought Communist
philosophy seemed fair.
Tuesday I was Socialist –
convinced by the au pair!
Wednesday the Lib Democrats
seemed sanest on defence.
Thursday the Conservatives
pledged tax cuts – twenty pence!
Last night the Raving Loonies
seemed most reasonable on air.
But today the Greens pledged
they would save our atmosphere.
I'd better buy the Sundays,
read their views and make a note –
Cos Monday I'll be eighteen
and be old enough to vote.

Philip Waddell

More Than I Wear

(for the young women in the Asian Women's Resource Association)

A young woman, Asian and British,
I have swallowed the world's rough oyster
    – pearl and all; yes, pearl and all.

I've had hard times and will face worse times,
but my gear is sorted and, sister,
    right now, I'm having a ball!

I move to Indi-pop and bhangra,
dupatta flying from my shoulder –
    angel wings and waterfall.

    The world is my oyster – pearl and all.
    Sister, right now, I'm having a ball!

Dadiji gave me this hand-stitched chunni.
Her love flows through it like a river,
    and I float tall – I float tall.

    The world is my oyster – pearl and all.
    Sister, right now, I'm having a ball!

I bought myself this denim jacket
and embroidered a lotus flower
    – there's none like it in the mall!

    The world is my oyster – pearl and all.
    Sister, right now, I'm having a ball!

My silk kameez glows with gold sequins
my satin salwar mirrors the hour
in Halifax and Bengal.

The world is my oyster – pearl and all.
Sister, right now, I'm having a ball!

My Doc Martins pack a feisty kick.
I am from Bradford and Jullunder,
Mirpur, Punjab and Walsall.

The world is my oyster – pearl and all.
Sister, right now, I'm having a ball!

I'm more than I wear: Asian British.
My clothes are those that eye the future,
with respect for tradition's power.
Sari or jeans, I am the daughter
of Birmingham and Southall.

The world is my oyster – pearl and all.
Sister, right now, I'm having a ball!
Sister, right now, I'm having a ball!

Debjani Chatterjee

Pop Idol

A wannabe singer called Trevor
Entered a contest to sing, yeah?
But, like, he didn't win it.
Cos they rigged it, innit!
It was rubbish. He came last. Whatever.

Roger Stevens

Acknowledgements

More than I Wear by Debjani Chatterjee first
published in *Namaskar: New and Selected Poems,*
Redbeck Press, 2004.

All poems are reproduced by permission of the
authors.

About nasen

Nasen is the leading UK professional association embracing all special and additional educational needs and disabilities. The organisation promotes the education, training, development and support of all those working within the special and additional educational needs and disabilities sector. Membership of nasen is an invaluable source of advice, offering an exclusive and vital range of benefits to support teachers, governors, teaching assistants and the entire education support network in the delivery of high quality inclusive practice.

Nasen contributes greatly and has a strong influence on policy and practice in the area of special educational needs through consultation and joint projects with government agencies and other professional bodies.

www.nasen.org.uk

welcome@nasen.org.uk

Tel: 01827 311500

About the Compiler

Roger Stevens is a poet, writer, musician and artist. He lives in Brighton, where he can often be found sitting on the beach scribbling in his notebook, and in France, where he eats a lot of cheese.

He spends much time travelling around the UK and Europe performing his work and making people laugh. In the course of his work he has met many talented teenagers and has found that students with learning difficulties very often make pretty good poets. In this collection he brings together poetry written by teenagers and by some of the best adults writing for young people.

Roger has written many books, including several solo collections of poetry and novels, and regularly compiles poetry anthologies. His verse novel for teenagers, *The Journal of Danny Chaucer* (Orion), was broadcast on BBC Radio 4.

As well as writing and performing, Roger helps teachers to teach poetry and encourages everyone to read more poems. His award-winning website, *www.poetryzone.co.uk*, features poetry by young people along with competitions, interviews with famous poets and educational resources.

Roger is really pleased to be working with nasen.

Also by Roger Stevens, published by A&C Black:

A Million Brilliant Poems (Part One)
On My Way to School I Saw A Dinosaur
The Secret Life of Pants
Let's Recycle Grandad

About the nasen Inclusive Poetry Competition

The nasen Inclusive Poetry Competition, on the theme of inclusion, was inspired by a poem about inclusion sent to Lorraine Petersen, CEO of nasen, from Whitfield and Aspen Primary School in Dover. The competition allowed all young people the opportunity to express their feelings on inclusion and how it has affected their lives. The children's poems are a powerful conductor of 'pupil voice' and provide food for thought for all those working with young people.

The following poems were selected from the competition winners for this voume:

Let Me Be Involved *Luke Petty*
Respect *Lewis Armour*
Inclusion *Jenny Davenport*
Difficult Times *Bret Linsdell*
My Life *Amy Staff*